Passover

THE FESTIVAL OF FREEDOM

by Sophia N. Cedarbaum   Pictures by Clare & John Ross

Union of American Hebrew Congregations

PASSOVER

The Festival of Freedom

PASSOVER comes in the spring.

It is the time of year when the birds fly back from the south.

It is the time of year when the flowers begin to blossom; when the whole world is glad to be alive.

Boys and girls, their mothers and fathers also like to have something new. They buy new spring outfits which they wear on Passover at the Seder, at the temple, and when they go visiting.

4

Passover lasts for seven days.

The first night of Passover is Seder night.

Very often several families get together for the Seder celebration.

The Seder table is a lovely sight.

Debbie and Danny are very proud that they are permitted to set the Seder table.

First they put the gleaming white tablecloth on the table. They make sure that it fits properly and that it hangs evenly.

They set the places with the family's nicest silver and dishes.

In the center of the table they put a low vase of spring flowers.

Now they come to the part they like best—

putting the Passover cups and plates on the table.

They put the large wine goblet for the Prophet Elijah near the flowers.

At their father's place they put a plate on which are three matsos. The matsos are hidden in the folds of a matso cover.

Next to the matsos they place the Seder plate. Their Seder plate is a very beautiful one that their grandmother brought from Europe many years ago. It is made of heavy silver and has figures on it showing all sorts of Passover scenes. It also has little scooped-out places for all the things that belong on the plate:

the roasted bone,
the roasted egg,
the bitter herbs,
the parsley,
the *charoses*.

At each place they put:

a sauce dish of salt water
>in which the parsley will be
>dipped,

a wine glass
>which will be filled four times
>during the Seder,

a Haggadah,
>the book which contains the
>Seder service and the story
>of Passover.

They put a pillow on father's armchair.

The Seder is a dinner party.

The Seder is like a play. There are speaking parts for children and adults, there are singing parts, and there are action parts.

The Seder is like a service in the temple, a service in which we thank God that we are not slaves.

SABBATH CANDLES

Mother blesses the holiday candles:

BORUCH ATO ADONOY
ELOHENU MELECH HO-OLOM
ASHER KID'SHONU B'MITSVOSOV
V'TSIVONU L'HADLIK NER SHEL
YOM TOV.

BLESSED ARE YOU, O LORD OUR GOD,
    KING OF THE WORLD,
WHO HAS MADE US HOLY BY YOUR
    COMMANDMENTS
AND HAS COMMANDED US TO KINDLE
    THE HOLIDAY LIGHTS.

Father chants the Passover Kiddush.

Mother, the guests, and the children join
in the blessing over the wine:

BORUCH ATO ADONOY
ELOHENU MELECH HO-OLOM
BORE PRI HAGOFEN.

BLESSED ARE YOU, O LORD OUR GOD,

13

KING OF THE WORLD, WHO CREATES
THE FRUIT OF THE VINE.

They sip the wine. The children, of course, drink grape juice.

The parsley is passed to everyone at the table. They dip the parsley into the salt water and together they say the blessing:

BLESSED ARE YOU, O LORD OUR GOD, KING OF THE WORLD, WHO CREATES THE FRUIT OF THE EARTH.

Danny loves the tangy taste of the parsley. He finishes Debbie's portion as well as his own.

Father takes the middle matso from the matso cover. He breaks it and wraps one half in a napkin. This is called the *afikomon*. It will provide much fun for the children before the Seder is over.

Debbie and Danny are the youngest at the Seder. They ask the Four Questions.

MA NISHTANO HALEILO HAZE MIKOL HALELOS?

WHY IS THIS NIGHT DIFFERENT FROM ALL OTHER NIGHTS?

WHY DO WE EAT MATSO AND NOT BREAD?

WHY DO WE EAT BITTER HERBS?

Danny asks the last two questions.

Father answers these questions.

He reads from the Haggadah.

"Many years ago, the Jewish people were slaves. They were owned by the Pharaohs, the rulers of Egypt. The Pharaohs liked to build big cities with palaces and pyramids. The slaves had to do this work. They worked for long hours in the blazing sun. They were treated very cruelly. They were whipped and were always made to work much faster and harder.

17

"Then God sent Moses to lead the Jewish people out of Egypt.

"Moses came to the Pharaoh and said, 'Let my people go out of Egypt.'

"Pharaoh did not want to lose his slaves. But at last he agreed to let them go. Then he changed his mind. He broke his promise many times before he finally let the Jews leave Egypt."

Debbie and Danny lead in singing "Dayenu":

I-LU HO-TSI-O-NU MI-MITS-RA-IM, DAYENU.

IF GOD HAD BROUGHT US OUT OF EGYPT,
IT WOULD HAVE BEEN ENOUGH!

Debbie and Danny are eager for their first taste of matso for this season. They love the crunchiness of unleavened bread.

Debbie leads in reciting Ha-Motsi.

Danny leads in saying the blessing for the matso.

BORUCH ATO ADONOY
ELOHENU MELECH HO-OLOM
ASHER KID'SHONU B'MITSVOSOV
V'TSIVONU AL ACHILAS MATSO.

BLESSED ARE YOU, O LORD OUR GOD,
KING OF THE WORLD, WHO HAS MADE
US HOLY BY YOUR COMMANDMENTS
AND COMMANDED US TO EAT MATSO.

And now comes the dinner. Mother certainly is a good cook! Everyone says these are the best matso balls that they have ever eaten.

During the dinner there is lively conversation. Uncle David tells of the Seder he attended in Israel. It was in a children's vil-

lage. The children had come from many different lands. They were very happy to be celebrating the Seder in Israel.

Danny has been sitting quietly, lost in thought. Suddenly he breaks in.

"I wonder how it would feel to be a slave?"

"If we were slaves you would not have a collection of automobile models and I would not have any pretty dresses to wear," answered Debbie.

"Why not?" asked Danny.

"Because dresses and models cost money and Daddy would not have any money."

"He could work and earn money, couldn't he?"

"He could work, but if he were a slave he would not get paid. He would have to work for his master. This master would own Daddy, and us, too, as if we were animals. Daddy would have to do everything the master wanted him to do without getting paid."

"Isn't that right, Daddy?" asked Debbie, turning to her father.

"Yes, it is," he answered.

"Well, then Daddy could go to work for somebody else."

"No, he could not. A slave cannot change masters. It is the master who decides what the slave has to do. When you belong to a master you do what he wants you to do. You must live where he says you should. You eat the food he gives you. You can never go anywhere. You are never free to do the things you want to do. Besides, you have to work very hard all day long without rest."

"Well, I am certainly glad that I am not a slave," says Danny.

"So are we all," agrees his father. "That is why we celebrate Passover."

A favorite part of the Seder is the treasure hunt. Ever since father broke the middle matso the children have tried to keep an eye on the afikomon. They were sure that this year they would catch father in the act of hiding the matso. But he was too quick for them again. Now they have to search. But where?

Father gives them clues. He tells them when they are "hot" or "cold."

Oh! Oh! Debbie has found the afikomon. She gets the prize and everyone gets a little piece of the afikomon to eat.

The meal is over. They say Grace.

BLESSED ARE YOU, O LORD OUR GOD, KING OF THE WORLD, WHO GIVES FOOD TO ALL.

Danny opens the door for the Prophet Elijah. The children watch Elijah's cup very closely to see whether any of the wine will disappear.

Now more songs are sung. Debbie and Danny know all the Seder songs.

They sing loud and clear.

They sing:

"Ey-lee-yo-hu ha-na-vi"

and

"Adir hu."

"Echod mi yodea" is a lot of fun as you keep adding numbers and singing faster and faster.

"Who knows one . . .?
Who knows two . . .?
Who knows three . . .?"

As for "Chad Gadyo," no one has much breath left after that song is finished!

Debbie and Danny are sleepy and tired. They are worn out but happy. Their heads nod as the grown-ups finish the Seder service with this prayer:

Now we come to the end of our Seder service.

As we celebrated this Festival tonight, so may we celebrate it, all of us together, next year again, in joy, in peace and in freedom.

The Seder is over.

Everyone has had a wonderful time.

We hope that you, too, will enjoy your Seder.

HAPPY PASSOVER!